Making up Your Mind

by Linda Kita-Bradley

Grass Roots Press

Making up Your Mind
© Grass Roots Press 2020
www.grassrootsbooks.net

Acknowledgements

Grass Roots Press acknowledges the financial support of the Government of Canada for our publishing activities.

Canada

Produced with the assistance of the Government of Alberta through the Alberta Media Fund.

Alberta

Editor: Dr. Pat Campbell
Photography: Susan Rogers
Book design: Lara Minja, Lime Design Inc.

Library and Archives Canada Cataloguing in Publication

Title: Making up your mind / by Linda Kita-Bradley.

Names: Kita-Bradley, Linda, 1958- author.

Series: Kita-Bradley, Linda, 1958- Soft skills at work.

Description: Series statement: Soft skills at work

Identifiers: Canadiana 20200212168 | ISBN 9781771533430 (softcover)

Subjects: LCSH: Readers for new literates. | LCSH: Readers—Decision making. | LCGFT: Readers (Publications)

Classification: LCC PE1126.N43 K58 2020 | DDC 428.6/2—dc23

Part 1

Joe works in a hardware store.

He mixes and sells paint.

Joe is bored with his job.

But Joe is a manager.
He is proud of that.

And he gets a good paycheck.

Joe looks at the job board.

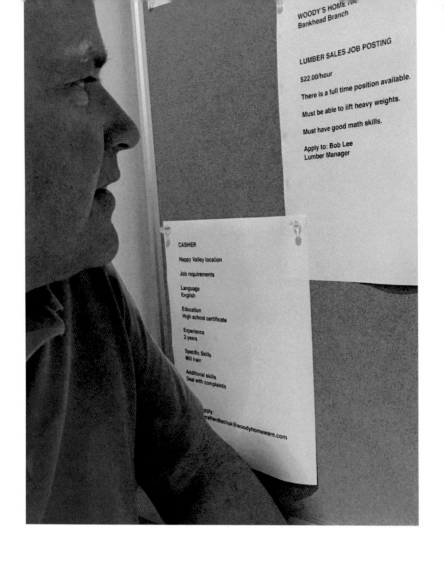

Oh! There is a job in the lumberyard.

Joe can work outside.

Joe watches Pete work.
Pete is Joe's best friend.

Pete lifts heavy lumber.

Pete drives a forklift.

Joe drives home.
He thinks about the job.

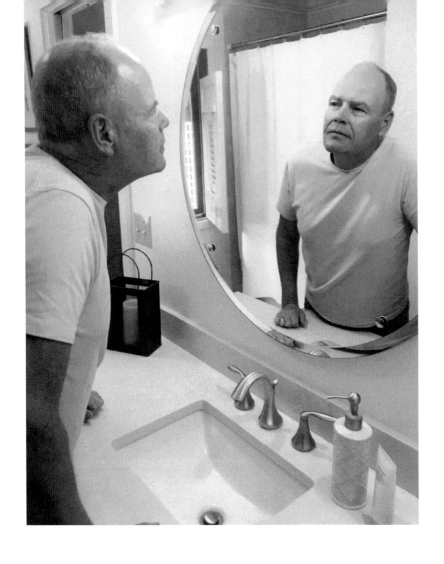

Joe looks in the mirror.
Is he too old for this job?

Joe drives to work.
He thinks about the job.

"The work is hard.
And I will make less money."

Apply? Yes? No?

Joe is good at his job.

But the new job?
Is the forklift hard to drive?

But Joe can work with Pete.
He likes that.

Joe checks the job board again.

Where is that job?

The job is gone.
Darn!

Talking About the Story

1. Joe has a hard time making up his mind. Explain why.

2. Imagine you are Joe. Would you apply for the job? Why or why not?

3. What do you do when you cannot make up your mind?

Part 2

Read the next story about Joe.

How is it different from the first story?

Joe works in a hardware store.

He is bored with his job.

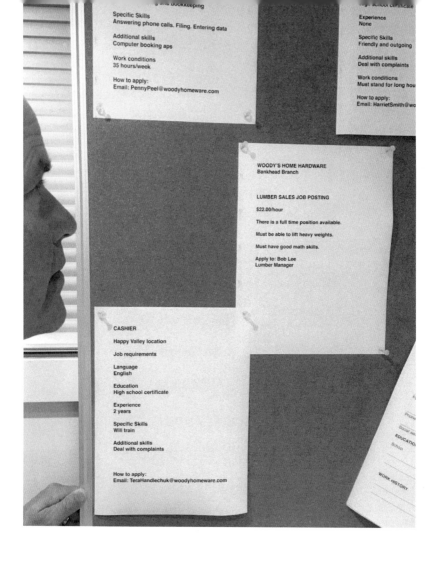

Joe checks the job board.

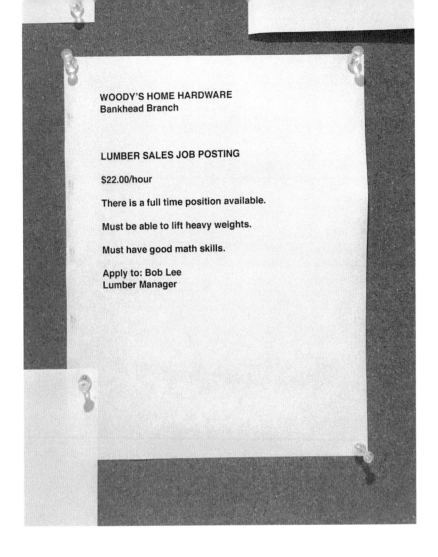

WOODY'S HOME HARDWARE
Bankhead Branch

LUMBER SALES JOB POSTING

$22.00/hour

There is a full time position available.

Must be able to lift heavy weights.

Must have good math skills.

Apply to: Bob Lee
Lumber Manager

Oh! There is a job in the lumberyard.

Joe's paycheck will be less.

But Joe wants to work outside.

Joe makes two lists.
He thinks of all the reasons to apply.

I will work with my best friend.

I will work outside.

I will lift heavy lumber.
I will be strong.

I will measure things.
My math will be better.

Joe lists reasons not to apply.

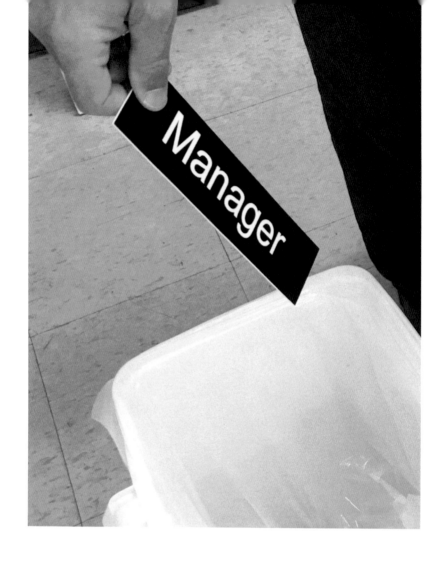

I will not be a manager.
I will make less money.

The forklift scares me.

Joe talks to his wife.

She says, "We can live on less money.
We can take the bus to work."

Joe talks to Pete.

Pete says, "Don't worry.
The forklift is easy to drive."

Joe thinks about the job.
The forklift still scares him.

But Joe's gut says, "Apply!"

Joe applies for the job.

Made in the USA
Monee, IL
09 June 2022